NANI

DAVID

STITCH AND LILO

Published by Scholastic Inc.,
90 Old Sherman Turnpike, Danbury, Connecticut 06816
by arrangement with Disney Licensed Publishing.

SCHOLASTIC and associated logos are trademarks of Scholastic Inc.

ISBN 0-7172-6661-3   Printed in the U.S.A.

DISNEY'S
Lilo & Stitch

SCHOLASTIC INC.

New York   Toronto   London   Auckland   Sydney
Mexico City   New Delhi   Hong Kong   Buenos Aires

In a far-off galaxy, an alien scientist named Jumba had created a strange creature called Experiment 626. Because 626 was always destroying things, he was being sent to prison by the Grand Councilwoman. But 626 managed to escape!

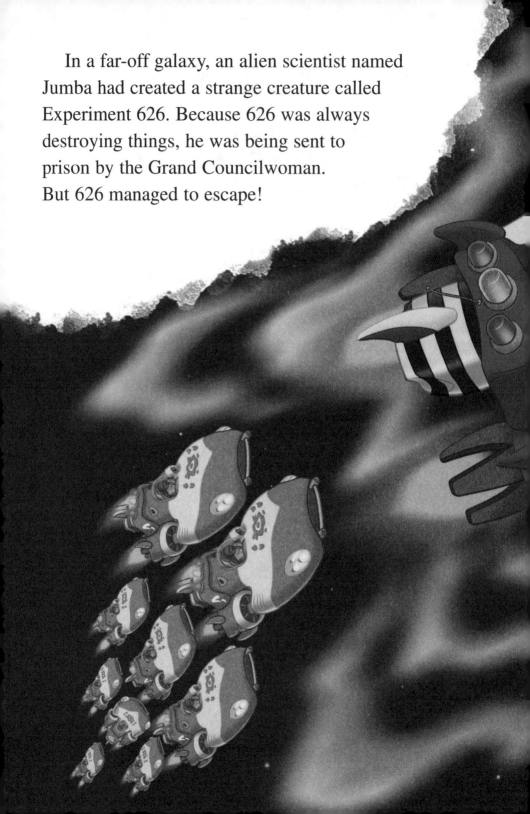

Now 626 was headed for Earth.
The Grand Councilwoman sent Jumba
and Pleakley, another alien, on a mission:
To capture 626 and bring him back.

Meanwhile on Earth, a
five-year-old Hawaiian girl
named Lilo was also on a
mission—she was feeding a
peanut-butter sandwich to a fish named
Pudge. Lilo thought it was very important to
do this, because she believed Pudge controlled
the weather. Unfortunately, Lilo was now late
for her hula dance lesson.

Lilo rushed into her dance class, dripping water on the floor. Her classmates began to slip and slide.

"Stop, stop," cried the hula instructor. He asked Lilo why she was late and wet. The little girl tried to explain about Pudge.

"You're crazy," said Myrtle, one of Lilo's classmates. Lilo pounced on Myrtle. The instructor quickly pulled them apart.

The instructor called Lilo's sister, Nani, to take Lilo home. Nani was Lilo's only family. But when Nani arrived, Lilo had already left! Nani panicked because a social worker was arriving this afternoon to decide whether Lilo could continue to live with Nani.

But Lilo was already at home listening to Elvis Presley music. She was sad because none of her classmates wanted to be her friend.

Lilo was so upset she locked her sister out of the house. Nani was still trying to get in when the social worker, Cobra Bubbles, arrived.

Once inside, the visit went from bad to worse. Cobra told Nani that she had three days to prove that she could take care of Lilo properly. Otherwise, Lilo would be taken away.

Later that evening, Nani and Lilo were talking in Lilo's room. Suddenly something lit up the sky outside.

"A falling star!" Lilo shouted excitedly. She pushed Nani out of her room. Lilo wanted to make a wish in private.

But Nani still listened as Lilo whispered, "It's me again. I need someone to be my friend. Maybe send me an angel . . . the nicest angel you have."

But what Lilo had really seen was 626's spaceship crashing into Earth! 626 stepped out of the smoking crater. He cackled with delight. He headed down a dark road—only to be run over by some trucks and knocked out. When he woke up the next morning—none the worse for wear—the indestructible 626 found he was in an animal rescue home. Before long, he realized that Jumba and Pleakley were after him.

That same morning, Nani and Lilo went to the animal rescue home to find a pet. Nani hoped it would cheer Lilo up.

When Lilo came in, 626 tried to look as much like a dog as he could. Lilo was his only way to escape from Jumba and Pleakley. So he hugged Lilo and won her heart.

"What is that thing?" Nani cried when she saw 626.

"A dog, I think," the rescue lady answered nervously.

Despite Nani's protests, Lilo adopted her new "dog" and named him "Stitch."

Meanwhile, Jumba and Pleakley were watching as Nani and Lilo left with Stitch.

Jumba wanted to capture 626 right away. But Pleakley reminded his partner that they could not be seen.

"We have to blend in," Pleakley told him.

After Nani left for work,
Lilo tried to teach Stitch to
fetch. But Stitch was not
interested in being
trained. Lilo ended
up fetching for
Stitch instead.

Then Lilo bought two snow cones. Stitch ended up
dumping his on the head of a small dog. Stitch was not
exactly what Lilo had expected.

Dressed like tourists, Jumba and Pleakley were
nearby watching Stitch. They were waiting for their
chance to capture him.

Later that day, Lilo and Stitch sat in the restaurant where Nani worked. Lilo finished drawing in her sketchbook and held it up to Stitch. "This is you," she told him. "This is your badness level. It's unusually high for someone your size. We need to fix that."

Jumba and Pleakley were also sitting in the restaurant. They lured Stitch over to their table. While Jumba grabbed Stitch and tried to place his alien handcuffs on the creature, Stitch opened his mouth wide and swallowed Pleakley's head. Nani had to dump a pitcher of iced tea on Stitch to make him let go.

When the restaurant owner found out that Stitch belonged to Nani, he pointed to the door. "This is not working out," he told Nani.

Nani and Lilo took Stitch home.

"This is a great home. You'll like it a lot!" Lilo told Stitch. She gave him a pillow so he could sleep on the floor. Stitch shredded the pillow. Then he went to the kitchen, where he made another mess.

Nani had had enough! She grabbed Stitch saying, "We have to take him back."

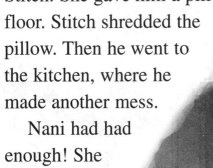

"He was an orphan and we adopted him!" said Lilo. "What about *'ohana?*"

Nani stopped. Their father had taught them about *'ohana.*

" *'Ohana* means family," Lilo continued. "Family means nobody . . ."

" . . . gets left behind . . . or forgotten. I know. I know," Nani said, sighing.

Stitch jumped from Nani's arms, and he and Lilo went into Lilo's room.

Stitch
climbed onto
Lilo's bed
and found a
photograph
of her family
under the
pillow.

"Be careful
of that!" Lilo
warned. The picture was all she had left of her father
and mother. She snatched it back and slipped the
precious photo back underneath her pillow.

So Stitch amused himself with other things in Lilo's
room. He built a model city—and then destroyed it.

In the middle of the night, Stitch woke Lilo and showed her a picture in a book he had found.

"That's the Ugly Duckling." Lilo yawned. "See? He's sad because he is all alone, and nobody wants him."

Lilo pointed to another page.

So Nani set out to find a new job with Lilo and
Stitch in tow. First, she went to a local grocery store.
While Nani spoke to the owner, Lilo tried to teach
Stitch to behave.

"Elvis Presley was a model citizen," Lilo explained.
"I've compiled a list of his traits for you to practice.
Number one is dancing." Unfortunately, their dance
routine knocked over the owner, so Nani didn't get the job.

While Nani tried to get a job at a coffee shop, Lilo continued with Stitch's lessons.

"Number two: Elvis played guitar," she said as she handed Stitch a ukulele. But when Stitch played the instrument, the piercing high notes shattered glass. Nani didn't get that job either.

Finally, as Nani tried to get a job as a lifeguard, Lilo prepared Stitch for his last lesson. "Time to bring it all together," she told him.

Stitch began to play his ukulele. Tourists began to crowd around him to take pictures. But their camera flashes upset Stitch, who caused a commotion. Nani, once again, did not get the job.

Everything had gone wrong. The unhappy sisters sat
down on the beach. David, a friend of Nani's, saw them.
To cheer them up, David
suggested they all
go surfing. The
group headed
for the waves.

Once she began to surf, Nani forgot all her troubles. Stitch clapped his paws, and David and Lilo laughed as they enjoyed the waves. For a little while, everyone was happy.

But as Nani, Lilo, and Stitch
rode a large wave, Jumba sneaked up behind them.
Jumba grabbed Stitch and pulled him under the water.
Desperate, Stitch grabbed Lilo and began dragging her
down. David and Nani pulled Lilo to safety, never
noticing the aliens. Stitch
finally won his struggle
with Pleakley and
Jumba, but he
was exhausted.
Luckily, David
went back and
rescued Stitch.

Back on the beach, Nani frantically checked to make sure Lilo was okay. Nani looked up to see Cobra Bubbles watching. He had seen the whole thing! Nani asked David to watch Lilo. Then Cobra quietly told Nani that although he knew she was trying, it was time to find a more suitable home for Lilo.

That night, Lilo studied her family photo. "Our family's little now, but if you want, you could be part of it," she said to Stitch.

Stitch wanted to belong, but he knew he had already caused too much trouble. While Lilo watched, Stitch took *The Ugly Duckling* book and climbed out of the window and into the night.

Stitch walked into the forest.
He opened the storybook to the pages
that Lilo had shown him. Just like the
Ugly Duckling, Stitch felt alone.
"I'm lost!" he cried.

The next morning, a very unhappy Grand Councilwoman fired Pleakley and Jumba. But Jumba was pleased. Now he could capture Stitch *his* way.

Soon Jumba found Stitch in the forest. Stitch didn't run. But he wouldn't go with Jumba either.

"Waiting," Stitch told Jumba.

"For what?" Jumba asked impatiently.

"Family," replied Stitch.

"You're built to destroy. You can never belong," Jumba said.

Stitch dropped the book and ran!

Meanwhile, Lilo joined Nani in the kitchen for breakfast. "Stitch left," Lilo murmured sadly.

Nani comforted Lilo. Now it would be harder to tell Lilo that they would be living apart.

But suddenly, David burst in saying, "I think I've found you a job!"

This was Nani's last chance to keep Lilo. She rushed out with David, telling Lilo to stay inside and not to let anyone in.

At the same time, Stitch was racing to
Lilo's house with Jumba following close
behind. Stitch slipped through
the dog door. Jumba crashed
through the front door.

Frightened, Lilo
called Cobra Bubbles.
"Aliens are attacking
my house! They want
my dog!"

Jumba and Stitch
fought so hard that they
destroyed the house!

Meanwhile, Nani got the job at the general store down the street. As she left, a fire engine shrieked past. Fearing the worst, Nani raced home.

Cobra Bubbles was already there.
Lilo was in his car. Nani begged
Cobra not to take Lilo from
her. Cobra just pointed to
the ruined house and shook
his head. Lilo watched as
the two argued. Then she
slipped out of the car and into
the forest. Stitch followed her.

Stitch quickly found Lilo. Wanting to apologize,
he handed Lilo her scorched family photo, which he
had managed to save. But Lilo was angry at Stitch.

"You ruined everything!" she shouted.

Lost for words, Stitch transformed himself into
his alien form. Lilo finally understood. "You're one
of them?"

At that moment an alien
named Captain Gantu appeared. He had been sent by
the Grand Councilwoman to capture Stitch. He snared
both Stitch and Lilo and carried them to his spaceship.
Stitch escaped. But before he could free Lilo, Gantu's
ship took off.

By the time Nani arrived, she was too late. She
watched as the spaceship carrying her
sister disappeared into the sky.

Luckily, Stitch convinced Jumba and Pleakley to help him rescue Lilo. Soon Nani and the three aliens were in Jumba's spaceship battling Captain Gantu. After a wild chase, Stitch was able to free Lilo.

Jumba landed his spaceship on the waves behind David, who was surfing. David gave them all a ride to shore on his surfboard, though it took a few trips!

But their troubles were not over. Cobra Bubbles was waiting on the beach for Lilo. And alien troops were waiting for Stitch!

The Grand Councilwoman ordered the troops to place Stitch on her ship. Stitch asked if he could say good-bye to Lilo. The Councilwoman was shocked.

"This is my family," Stitch explained. "I found it all on my own. It's little and broken, but it's still good."

Then Lilo showed Stitch's adoption papers to the
Grand Councilwoman. A stickler for rules, she agreed
to let Stitch stay on Earth with Lilo. And Cobra decided
Lilo could stay with Nani.

Jumba and Pleakley stayed on Earth, too. Along with
David and Cobra Bubbles, they became part of Lilo's
new family, where no one ever gets left behind.